OTHER TITLES OF INTEREST

25 SIMPLE SHORTWAVE BROADCAST BAND AERIALS

by
E. M. NOLL

BERNARD BABANI (publishing) LTD
THE GRAMPIANS
SHEPHERDS BUSH ROAD
LONDON W6 7NF
ENGLAND

PLEASE NOTE

Although every care has been taken with the production of this book to ensure that any projects, designs, modifications and/or programs etc. contained herein, operate in a correct and safe manner and also that any components specified are normally available in Great Britain, the Publishers do not accept responsibility in any way for the failure, including fault in design, of any project, design, modification or program to work correctly or to cause damage to any other equipment that it may be connected to or used in conjunction with, or in respect of any other damage or injury that may be so caused, nor do the Publishers accept responsibility in any way for the failure to obtain specified components.

Notice is also given that if equipment that is still under warranty is modified in any way or used or connected with home-built equipment then that warranty may be void.

© 1984 BERNARD BABANI (publishing) LTD

First Published – January 1984
Reprinted – February 1989
Reprinted – January 1993

British Library Cataloguing in Publication Data
Noll, E. M.
25 simple shortwave broadcast band aerials.
1. Radio, Shortwave – Antennas
I. Title
621.3841'35   TK7871.6

ISBN 0 85934 107 0

Printed and bound in Great Britain by Cox & Wyman Ltd, Reading

ABOUT THE AUTHOR

Ed Noll is an established American technical author who has written many books, articles and instruction manuals as well as having lectured and taught radio communications at various universities in the U.S.A.

He has worked on the staff of a number of broadcasting stations and as a consulting engineer.

CONTENTS

SAFETY

The safety of an installation is your responsibility when erecting an aerial. The hazards are electrical shock, injury to a person or damage to property. Be thoughtful and wise. Do not erect an aerial where it can come in contact with, or fall upon electrical wires while you are making the installation or if it breaks loose from wind damage or fatigue after you have made the installation. Erect your aerial carefully so it cannot fall upon an individual or damage property during or after erection. As an extra safety precaution insulated wire is recommended.

In the construction of a long-wire aerial chose a wire gauge that is low enough to prevent breakage under wind and erection stress. Good-quality tough insulation adds to the strength of a wire under stress.

PERSPECTIVE

Your aerial is the sensor that is activated by radio signals reaching your location from all parts of the world. Modern short-wave receivers are so sensitive that built-in, indoor and very simple outdoor aerials derive adequate signals from many of the high-powered radio broadcast stations. However, there are a number of advantages in having a well-planned efficient outdoor aerial system. Such an aerial is important in receiving weak broadcast signals particularly when you are trying to make a positive identification. If you are interested in receiving the very best signal from both strong and weak incoming signals, the aerial is important in minimizing the ill-effects of fast fading, background interference and selective-fading (distortion resulting from some frequencies that comprise an incoming signal fading in-and-out relative to others). For example, a solid lock-in signal is preferred by the avid music fan. A good aerial can aid in the minimization of signal-generated (QRM) and static (QRN) interference. More than one station may occupy the same frequency or, a signal on an adjacent channel may be especially strong, producing objectionable interference. Often a directional aerial is helpful in emphasizing a desired signal and attenuating an undesired one. Fortunately good aerials can be erected at low cost, and for a small fractional part of the cost of your receiving equipment. This books tells the story.

A series of 25 aerials are covered. However it is helpful if you start by reading the Perspective and the discussions about the first ten aerial types presented. Many of the principles, ideas and construction procedures covered can be used again in the planning of the aerials that follow.

You may wish to check and compare two or more aerials to find one best suited to your needs and location. To compare one aerial to another, do so directly using a coaxial switch or some other means of making a fast changeover. You cannot make an accurate comparison by taking one aerial down and replacing it with another because of the rapidity of propagation changes.

1

Short-Wave Bands

The official ITU shortwave bands are listed in Table 1. The 22-metre band is the latest one. The 90 and 120 metre bands are usually considered shortwave bands, however technically it is more appropriate to consider them as medium wave frequencies. This book will introduce several aerials for use on these two bands. It should be stressed that shortwave broadcast stations cannot only be found within the frequency limits of the official bands. A host of stations operate above and below the frequency limits and, to a limited extent, on other more widely separated frequencies. A few are pirate stations and not officially allocated by their countries.

Table 1   ITU Short-wave Bands

Band (metres)	Frequency (MHz)	Band (metres)	Frequency (MHz)
120	2.3 − 2.498	25	11.65 − 12.05
90	3.2 − 3.4	22	13.6 − 13.8
75	3.95 − 4.0	19	15.1 − 15.6
60	4.75 − 5.06	16	17.55 − 17.9
49	5.95 − 6.2	13	21.45 − 21.85
41	7.1 − 7.3	11	25.67 − 26.1
31	9.5 − 9.9		

Aerial Directivity

Many aerials, even the simpler types, have directional characteristics. Some aerials are highly directional and can be erected to favour specific continents and countries. In erecting a directional aerial it is important that you know the compass bearings of your particular erection site. An accurate compass is a big help. The second bit of information that you must know are the particular angles (azimuth) of the stations to be received from your site. Fortunately, most aerials that you would use for short-wave broadcast listening have a wide selectivity response and orientation is not especially critical. Nevertheless you can do some favouring that can be helpful. Details will follow later on.

Some typical receive angles from the capital cities of London, England; Ottawa, Canada; Canberra, Australia; Wellington, New Zealand and Washington, D.C., U.S.A. to eleven countries are given in Table 2. Most of the countries selected transmit at high power on several of the short-wave bands. Such stations can be of help in checking and comparing aerials. As mentioned previously, precise orientation for even rather highly directional aerials for short-wave broadcast reception are not critical except for narrow-beam vee-beams, rhombics and yagis. Orientation of 25° or more would be barely noticeable because of broad beam widths and strong incoming signals. Reception angles, mileage figures and a variety of data for more than 200 short-wave stations from your particular location can be obtained at low cost from Process Analysis Corp., 22nd Avenue, NW, Seattle, Washington, 98177, U.S.A.

If you plan to do a considerable amount of aerial testing a copy of the World Radio TV Handbook (WRTH) is very helpful. It can be purchased in almost any country of the world that has sales outlets for short-wave broadcast receiving equipment. Frequencies, schedules, powers and a vast amount of additional information are included.

Time Standard Stations
In addition to high powered broadcast stations there are a variety of stations that transmit time and frequency standard signals. Some of these stations are in, or adjacent to, several shortwave broadcast bands. Table 3 is a partial listing. Many of these stations are on the air continuously and can be easily identified. They are excellent for making aerial comparisons.

Time Zones
Another factor in making aerial checks and matching test time with the schedule of an overseas broadcast transmission is an understanding of time zones. The International Telecommunications Union has established Universal Time Coordinated (UTC) zone based on a 24-hour clock 0000 to 2400. This is the same as the long-used Greenwich Mean Time (GMT). Broadcast station schedules and short-wave listening newsletters and magazines use this universal time. It is your

Table 2   Typical Azimuth Angles to Sample Locations

Azimuth Angles From

Country/Town	London	Ottawa	Canberra	Wellington	Washington D.C.
Australia, Melbourne	74	268	–	268	257
Canada, Sackville	288	–	56	63	49
New Zealand, Wellington	20	248	113	–	243
England, London	–	53	315	342	49
USA, Washington D.C.	287	175	70	68	–
Brazil, Brasilia	226	150	159	135	147
China, Beijing	45	350	335	318	349
Germany, Cologne	95	52	312	324	44
Japan, Tokyo	31	331	352	332	330
Spain, Madrid	193	68	290	225	63
South Africa, Johannesburg	154	100	230	210	103
USSR, Moscow	64	34	316	312	32

Table 3
Aerial-checking Standard Time and Frequency Stations

USA Fort Collins, Colorado (WWV)
2.5 MHz − 5 MHz − 10 MHz − 15 MHz − 20 MHz
(continuous)

USA Kauai, Hawaii (WWVH)
2.5 MHz − 5 MHz − 10 MHz − 15 MHz
(continuous)

CANADA Ottawa, Ontario (CHU)
3.33 MHz − 7.335 MHz − 14.67 MHz
(continuous)

AUSTRALIA Lyndhurst, Victoria (VNG)
4.5 MHz   0945−2130 UTC
7.5 MHz   2245−2230 UTC
12 MHz   2145−0930 UTC

USSR Moscow (RWM)
4.996 MHz − 9.996 MHz − 14.996 MHz

responsibility to make the necessary conversion to local time. No such conversion is required for the United Kingdom except to add one hour during summer-time. Canada has six time zones. The number of hours to be subtracted from the UTC time is given in Table 4. Similar relations exist for the United States of America with the exception that the USA has only four time zones. As an example, when it is 12 noon (1200 UTC) in London, it is five hours earlier in Washington, D.C. (1200 − 0500) or 7 a.m. Time is advanced one hour for daylight time in each zone. New Zealand has only one time zone which is ahead of UTC by 12 hours. Midnight in London is noon in New Zealand. Australia has four time zones.

Aerial Chart
A dimension chart such as that given in Table 5 provides quick answers in your design of a receiving aerial. Values are given for each band 11 through 120 metres. The design frequency for each band is also given. Except for highly directional

Table 4 Universal Time and Time Zones

CANADIAN TIME ZONES

UTC	NEWFOUNDLAND		ATLANTIC	EST	CST	MST	PST
0000M	2030	8.30 PM	8 PM	7 PM	6 PM	5 PM	4 PM
0100	2130	9.30	9	8	7	6	5
0200	2230	10.30	10	9	8	7	6
0300	2330	11.30	11	10	9	8	7
0400	0030	12.30	12 M	11	10	9	8
0500	0130	1.30 AM	1 AM	12 M	11	10	9
0600	0230	2.30	2	1 AM	12 M	11	10
0700	0330	3.30	3	2	1 AM	12 M	11
0800	0430	4.30	4	3	2	1 AM	12 M
0900	0530	5.30	5	4	3	2	1 AM
1000	0630	6.30	6	5	4	3	2
1100	0730	7.30	7	6	5	4	3
1200N	0830	8.30	8	7	6	5	4
1300	0930	9.30	9	8	7	6	5
1400	1030	10.30	10	9	8	7	6
1500	1130	11.30	11	10	9	8	7
1600	1230	12.30 PM	12 N	11	10	9	8

6

1700	1.30 PM	1 PM	12 N	11AM	10 AM	9 AM
1800	2.30	2	1 PM	12 N	11	10
1900	3.30	3	2	1 PM	12 N	11
2000	4.30	4	3	2	1 PM	12 N
2100	5.30	5	4	3	2	1 PM
2200	6.30	6	5	4	3	2
2300	7.30	7	6	5	4	3
2400	8.30	8	7	6	5	4

USA TIME ZONES

UTC	EST	EST	EDT	CST	MST	PST
0000M	1900	7 PM	8 PM	6 PM	5 PM	4 PM
0100	2000	8	9	7	6	5
0200	2100	9	10	8	7	6
0300	2200	10	11	9	8	7
0400	2300	11	12 M	10	9	8
0500	2400	12 M	1 AM	11	10	9
0600	0100	1 AM	2	12 M	11	10

USA TIME ZONES (continued)

UTC	EST	EST	EDT	CST	MST	PST
0700	0200	2 AM	3 AM	1 AM	12 M	11 PM
0800	0300	3	4	2	1 AM	12 M
0900	0400	4	5	3	2	1 AM
1000	0500	5	6	4	3	2
1100	0600	6	7	5	4	3
1200N	0700	7	8	6	5	4
1300	0800	8	9	7	6	5
1400	0900	9	10	8	7	6
1500	1000	10	11	9	8	7
1600	1100	11	12 N	10	9	8
1700	1200	12 N	1 PM	11	10	9
1800	1300	1 PM	2	12 N	11	10
1900	1400	2	3	1 PM	12 N	11
2000	1500	3	4	2	1 PM	12 N
2100	1600	4	5	3	2	1 PM
2200	1700	5	6	4	3	2
2300	1800	6	7	5	4	3
2400	1900	7	8	6	5	4

8

AUSTRALIAN TIME ZONE

UTC	VICT	VICT	NA-SA	WA
0000M	1000	10 AM	9.30 AM	8 AM
0100	1100	11	10.30	9
0200	1200 N	12 N	11.30	10
0300	1300	1 PM	12.30 PM	11
0400	1400	2	1.30	12 N
0500	1500	3	2.30	1 PM
0600	1600	4	3.30	2
0700	1700	5	4.30	3
0800	1800	6	5.30	4
0900	1900	7	6.30	5
1000	2000	8	7.30	6
1100	2100	9	8.30	7
1200N	2200	10	9.30	8
1300	2300	11	10.30	9
1400	2400M	12 M	11.30	10
1500	0100	1 AM	12.30 AM	11
1600	0200	2	1.30	12 M
1700	0300	3	2.30	1 AM

AUSTRALIAN TIME ZONE (continued)

UTC	VICT	VICT	NA-SA	WA
1800	0400	4 AM	3.30 AM	2 AM
1900	0500	5	4.30	3
2000	0600	6	5.30	4
2100	0700	7	6.30	5
2200	0800	8	7.30	6
2300	0900	9	8.30	7
2400	1000	10	9.30	8

NEW ZEALAND TIME ZONE

UTC		
0000M		12 N
0100	1200 N	1 PM
0200	1300 PM	2
0300	1400	3
0400	1500	4
0500	1600	5
	1700	

10

0600	1800	6
0700	1900	7
0800	2000	8
0900	2100	9
1000	2200	10
1100	2300	11
1200N	2400 M	12 M
1300	0100 AM	1 AM
1400	0200	2
1500	0300	3
1600	0400	4
1700	0500	5
1800	0600	6
1900	0700	7
2000	0800	8
2100	0900	9
2200	1000	10
2300	1100	11
2400	1200 N	12 N

11

Table 5. *Dimensions, Spacings and Lengths*

Band	Frequency	1 λ	2 ½λ	3 ¼λ	4 0.1λ	5 0.15λ	6 0.2λ	7 ¼λ	8 ¾λ	9 Refl.	10 Dir.
Metres	MHz	ft.	ft.	ft.	ft.	ft.	ft.	ft.	ft.	ft.	ft.
120	2.4	410	205	103	41	62	82	98	296	205	180
90	3.3	298	149	75	30	45	60	71	215	149	132
75	4.0	246	123	62	25	37	49	59	178	123	113
60	5.0	197	98	49	20	30	40	47	142	98	89
49	6.0	164	82	41	16	25	33	39	118	82	73
41	7.2	137	68	34	14	20	27	33	98	68	62
31	9.7	101	51	25	10	15	20	24	73	51	45
25	12.0	82	41	21	8	12	16	20	59	41	37
22	13.7	72	36	18	7	11	14	17	52	36	32.5
19	15.3	64	32	16	6	10	12	15.5	46	32	29
16	17.7	55	28	14	5.5	8.5	11	13.5	40	28	25
13	21.6	46	23	11.5	5	7	9	11	33	23	20.5
11	26.0	38	19	9.5	4	5.5	7.5	9	27	19	17

12

aerials, lengths are relatively non-critical and little difference in performance is obtained when lengths depart as much as 15—20 percent. However, for directional aerials using parasitic reflectors and directors, use a tolerance no greater than about 3 percent. Columns 1—3 give the free-space dimensions of a full-wavelength, half-wavelength and quarter-wavelength. Columns 4—6 are useful in spacing phased aerials and parasitic aerial elements. Columns 7 and 8 show the dimensions for each quarter-wave side of a dipole aerial and each three-quarter-wave side of a three-halves wavelength aerial. Columns 9 and 10 show lengths for parasitic reflectors and directors. Equations used to calculate the various dimensions are as follows:

$$\lambda \text{Free Space} \qquad = 984/f_{MHz}$$
$$\lambda/2 \text{ Free Space} \qquad = 492/f_{MHz}$$
$$\lambda/4 \text{ Free Space} \qquad = 246/f_{MHz}$$
$$0.2\lambda \text{ Spacing} \qquad = 196/f_{MHz}$$
$$0.15\lambda \text{ Spacing} \qquad = 145.6/f_{MHz}$$
$$0.1\lambda \text{ Spacing} \qquad = 98.4/f_{MHz}$$
$$\lambda/4 \text{ Dipole} \qquad = 234/f_{MHz}$$
$$3/4\lambda \text{ Dipole} \qquad = 710/f_{MHz}$$
$$\text{Parasitic Reflector} \qquad = 492/f_{MHz}$$
$$\text{Parasitic Director} \qquad = 450/f_{MHz}$$

1. DIPOLE AND QUARTER—WAVE VERTICALS

These two aerial types are basic. Often they are used for reference aerials for making comparisons with other styles. Usually the dipole is mounted horizontally and fed at the centre. As shown in Fig.1a, each leg is one-quarter wavelength long, resulting in a half wavelength aerial. The feedline can be 300ohm line (TV transmission line) or 50—70ohm coaxial line. For receiver application a good match is not a demanding consideration as it would be if the aerial were used for both transmit and receive.

A half-wavelength dipole is able to detect signals coming in from all directions (all compass angles). However, it displays a maximum sensitivity to those signals that arrive perpendicular to, or broadside to the aerial wire as shown in Fig.1b. This horizontal sensitivity pattern has a figure-eight appearance. Theoretically, it has little or no sensitivity parallel to the aerial wire. In practice the actual pattern fills in and departs from the theoretical, and the aerial does display a reasonable sensitivity in all directions. The lower the aerial is mounted, the greater is the departure from the theoretical figure-eight.

When elevated properly above earth and placed well away from obstructions the vertical sensitivity pattern is a circle as shown. This pattern too is theoretical because the earth and height of the aerial above earth influence the vertical pattern.

In the reception of long-distance, short-wave signals it is helpful to have the vertical sensitivity pattern concentrated at low vertical angles extending between $0°$ and on up to not much more than $20°$. Short-wave radio signals in bouncing off the ionosphere return to the earth at these low angles. They are said to have a low wave angle. A receiving aerial does a better job of receiving such a low wave-angle signal if it too displays a maximum sensitivity at low vertical angles. Good low-angle results are obtained with a high aerial.

The fundamental vertical aerial is a quarter-wavelength long as shown in Fig.1c. The earth itself acts as a mirror quarter-wave segment. Earth conditions, in fact, have a great influence on the performance of a vertical antenna. The mirror segment of the quarter-wave vertical can be earth itself or a network of wires or conducting tubing that acts as a synthetic earth. If placed on the surface of the earth or a few inches below ground, such a low-resistance conducting surface can bring about a substantial improvement in aerial results. The use of a synthetic earth, called a ground plane, is also employed when the quarter-wave aerial is to be positioned high above the physical ground. In effect, the ground plane places an electrical reflection surface up at the level of the aerial.

The sensitivity patterns of a quarter-wave vertical are given in Fig.1c. The horizontal sensitivity pattern is circular, indicating that the aerial accepts signals arriving from all compass directions. The vertical sensitivity pattern approximates a figure-eight slashed lengthwise. Note that the maximum sensitivity is concentrated at low vertical angles below 45°. In fact, the net horizontal/vertical pattern is doughnut-like in appearance. In terms of DX reception, the low wave angle sensitivity is advantageous and can be obtained even though the aerial is mounted near earth level.

Two simple arrangements for a quarter-wave vertical are shown in Fig.1d. A reasonable low-resistance link to earth is attained by driving a pipe (6 feet or longer) into the earth. Also an earth radial system comprised of three or more quarter-wave conductors buried about two inches beneath the surface helps to improve sensitivity at low vertical angles. If desired the two earthing methods can be combined.

The required length for the quarter-wave segment of a half-wavelength aerial or the length of a quarter-wave vertical can be obtained from Table 5. The theoretical value for the aerial rešistance of a dipole is 72 ohms, while that of a quarter-wave vertical is 36 ohms. Again actual values depend upon height, ground conditions and other factors. Nevertheless both aerials can be used to supply signal to coaxial or flat lines in a receiving-only situation. In connecting a coaxial transmission line to a quarter-wave vertical, the inner conductor connects to the very bottom of the vertical aerial while the braid is connected to the pipe or other earthing system used.

Many of the aerials that follow are variations and/or elaborations of these fundamental types. The brief theoretical

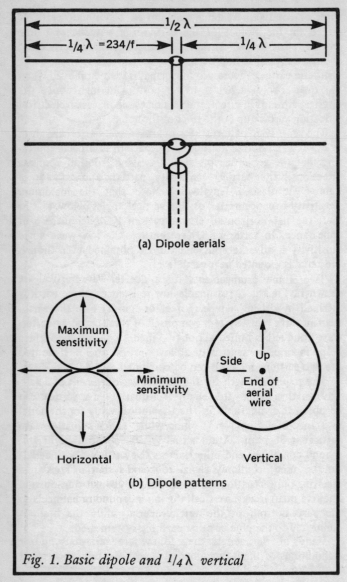

Fig. 1. Basic dipole and $1/4 \lambda$ vertical

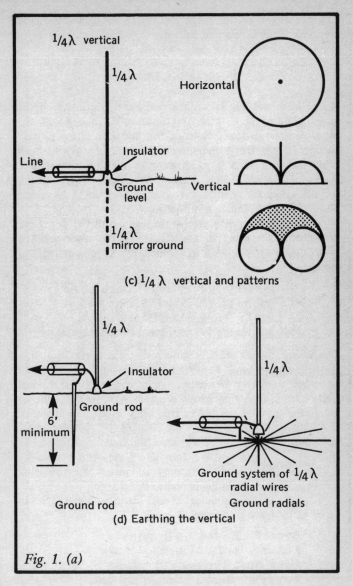

$1/4 \lambda$ vertical

$1/4 \lambda$

Horizontal

Line

Insulator

Ground level

Vertical

$1/4 \lambda$ mirror ground

(c) $1/4 \lambda$ vertical and patterns

$1/4 \lambda$

Insulator

Ground rod

6' minimum

$1/4 \lambda$

Ground system of $1/4 \lambda$ radial wires

Ground radials

Ground rod

(d) Earthing the vertical

Fig. 1. (a)

coverage of this section helps you better understand the basic concepts of the aerials that follow.

2. SLOPING DIPOLE

A sloping dipole, Fig.2, is a low cost and very effective dipole aerial. Only one high mounting location is required with the other end of the dipole fastened to a low post. The sensitivity pattern is essentially omnidirectional and responds to both horizontal and vertical polarization of the incoming signals. It responds well to low wave angle signals. When using a metallic support post, some users report some low-angle directivity in the direction of the slope.

The length of each quarter-wave segment of the sloper can be selected according to available mounting space and the particular bands you wish to accent a bit. Typical dimensions are as follows:

> 71   feet for the 120, 90 and 75 metre bands.
> 47   feet for the 60, 49 and 41 metre bands.
> 24   feet for the 31, 25 and 22 metre bands.
> 15.5 feet for the 19, 16, 13 and 11 metre bands.

The above figures do not imply that the aerials are only sensitive on the bands suggested. They are able to receive well on other bands too. Generally a short aerial will perform less well on lower frequency bands as compared to the performance on a long aerial on the higher frequency bands. For example, one with a 24 foot quarter-wave element will perform better on bands 19 through 11 metres than it does on bands 41 through 120 metres. A 47 foot sloper performs reasonably well on all of the bands 11 through 120 metres. Such an aerial would have an overall span of some 80 feet.

You can anticipate similar results for other aerial styles in terms of the band groupings

> *High* — Bands 7 through 19 metres
> *Medium* — Bands 22 through 31 metres.
> *Low* — Bands 41 through 60 metres
> *Very Low* — Bands 75 through 120 metres.

18

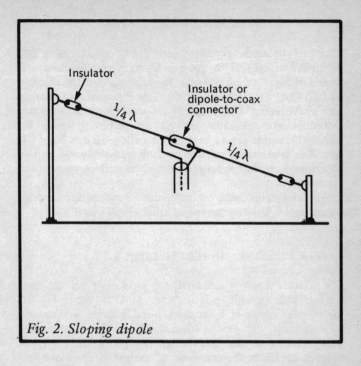

Fig. 2. Sloping dipole

In receive applications a variety of wire types can be used as an aerial e.g. single wire, stranded, single wire with insulation and stranded wire with insulation. Most of my aerial wires are PVC insulated types because of ease of erection, no noise problem when run through trees, and often more readily available and inexpensive at flea markets and surplus outlets. Electrical performance is not a consideration. Use a size that will take the mechanical mounting stress. For some aerial construction with little stress I use 24 SWG (22 AWG) insulated stranded. Popular with me for long aerials is solid insulated 16, 18 or 20 SWG (14, 16 or 18 AWG).

3. UNEVEN–LEG SLOPER

Fine performing compromise aerials can be erected using legs of unlike lengths. Two good-performing combinations are shown in Fig.3. In example (a) the high segment has a length of 15.5 feet, the lower leg, 24 feet. This combination performs well over bands 11 through 31. If space is available at the mounting site, an aerial for the low-frequency bands 41 through 120 metres can be made from lengths of 47 and 71 feet. This latter aerial will also perform reasonably well on the 11 through 31 metre bands but does require more erection space.

The idea of dissimilar leg length can be applied to a conventional dipole, inverted dipole and other aerials as well.

4. INVERTED DIPOLE

The inverted dipole is also a popular aerial style because only a single high mounting site is required. As shown in Fig. 4a the inverted dipole is fed at the top and includes two quarter-wave segments that extend down to low attachment positions. This modified dipole construction has performance characteristics similar to the conventional straight dipole. However, some directivity at low wave angles in the direction of each of the two sloping sides is attributed to this construction.

Element lengths for this aerial can be chosen according to Table 5 or selected according to the four special groupings mentioned in previous sections:

> *High* — 11, 13, 16, 19 metres
> *Medium* — 22, 25, 31 metres
> *Low* — 41, 49, 60, 75 metres
> *Very Low* — 90, 120 metres

Lengths to be chosen are, of course, also a function of the available space at your mounting site. Two separate inverted dipoles can be suspended from the same mast and supply signals to a single transmission line as shown in example (b). This top view shows the two aerials mounted in a perpendicular

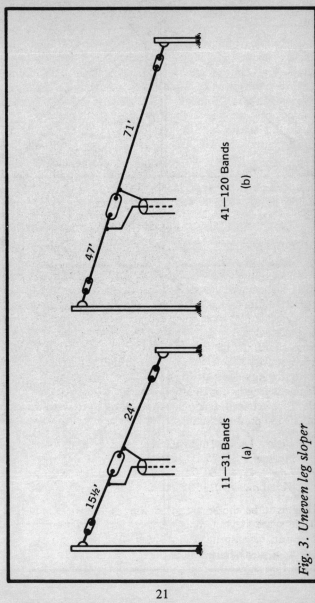

41—120 Bands

(b)

11—31 Bands

(a)

Fig. 3. Uneven leg sloper

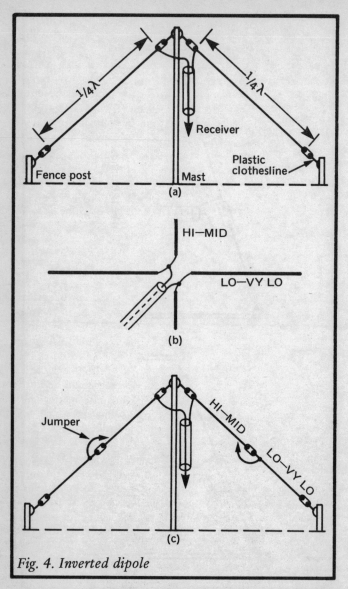

Fig. 4. Inverted dipole

22

fashion. Since the four segments are spaced equidistantly around the mast they can serve as guying for a reasonably high aerial pole.

An alternative plan of mounting for a long narrow mounting space is shown in example (c). In this arrangement the aerial elements are segmented. The top section has been cut for the high- and mid-frequency bands. When operation is desired on the lower frequency bands, jumpers are used to interconnect the two segments of each element. The overall length of each leg is cut for operation on the low-frequency and very low-frequency bands. Jumpers can be easily connected and disconnected because the end of each leg can be made readily accessible because of the low mounting position. If a high pole is constructed include a means of lowering and raising the apex of the inverted dipole.

5. UNEVEN–LEG INVERTED DIPOLE

Like the sloper, the inverted dipole configuration will perform well with uneven leg lengths as shown in Fig.5. In a typical installation lengths of 24 feet for one leg can be selected for bands 22 through 31 metres. The other leg would be cut for 15.5 feet encompassing bands 11 through 19 metres.

Such an aerial can also be used for the low-frequency bands assuming adequate mounting space. One leg could be cut to the length of 47 feet for bands 49 through 75 metres and a second leg of 71 feet for bands 90 and 120 metres.

6. INVERTED VEE 3/2-WAVELENGTH AERIAL

The aerial of Fig.6 is a good all-band performer. Each leg is 3/4 wavelength long on 31 metres. At the precise frequency for which it is cut it displays proper impedance for matching a coaxial or 300-ohm flat line. In fact, dipole constructions that have leg lengths that are odd multiples of a quarter-wavelength give a favorable low impedance at the centre feedpoint.

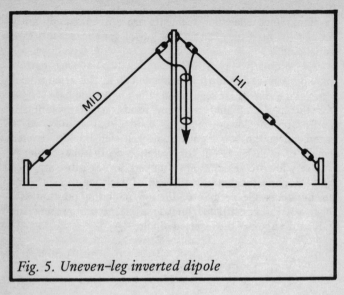

Fig. 5. Uneven–leg inverted dipole

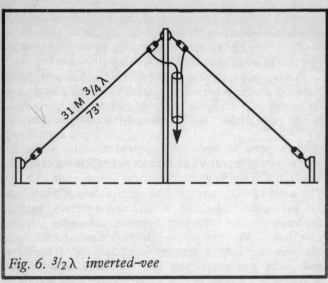

Fig. 6. ³/₂λ inverted–vee

The example of Fig.6 was cut to have 3/4 wavelength legs on the 31 metré band. Good to acceptable results were obtained on bands 11 through 31 metres. Omnidirectional performance was good and the aerial indicated some low wave angle directivity off the ends.

The aerial also did well on bands 41 through 120 metres. Note that its element length of 73 feet corresponds to a quarter wavelength on 90 metres. Thus on this frequency it operated as a conventional inverted dipole. If you have the space available you can expect proper results from this simple aerial construction.

7.   HELICAL VERTICAL

You have a confined mounting space. Try a vertical. A very low cost and effective vertical can be constructed from insulated hook-up wire and PVC (polyvinyl chloride) piping. This piping is a good high-frequency insulator and is lightweight.

An 11 through 19 metre helical vertical construction is shown in Fig.7. This simple vertical also produced acceptable results on 22 through 31 metres as well. The helical wire was made of 24 SWG (22 AWG) stranded wire. The support was a ten foot length of 1¼ inch outside diameter PVC piping. At the mounting site the PVC piping was held by a TV aerial mast clamp attached to the vent pipe of the house.

The wire length was 15½ feet corresponding to a quarter-wavelength on 19 metres. For a permanent installation very small diameter screw-eyes are screwed into the piping. Use 4-inch spacing and drill small starter holes. Spacing must be a little closer at the very top to consume the complete 15.5 foot length of wire. For easy experimentation at very little cost you can use carpet tacks. You may wish to try this initially to determine the PVC vertical best suited to your needs.

A short distance above the position where the mast clamp will hold the piping, drill two holes through the piping. These should be spaced about 1½" apart. The two bolts will serve as connection points. The helix wire and the inner conductor

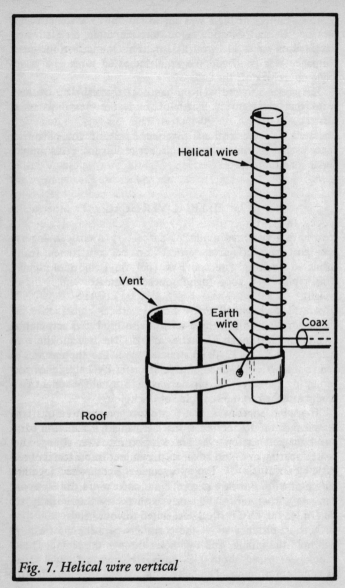

Fig. 7. Helical wire vertical

of the coaxial line are fixed to the top bolt. The lower bolt is the connection point for the coaxial shield and an earth wire that is connected to the mast clamp. This connection then uses the vent piping system of the house as an earth. TV transmission line can be used as well.

In winding the helix make one loop immediately beneath each head as the wire is laced around the piping in helical fashion.

Piping is normally available in any number of inner diameter and outer-diameter sizes up to 3 inches ID and perhaps even wider if such is required. Many of the sizes telescope rather snugly and can be bolted together to increase the height of the construction. As a result a higher vertical can be built. Such piping can also be used as a mast support for other aerial types. In fact it provides a light-weight and insulated mast. For masts 30 foot or higher, inexpensive rope (nylon) guying can be used.

8. EARTH MOUNTED HELICALS

Two or three ten-foot sections of telescoping PVC piping can be bolted together and earth-mounted. The base for this type of vertical is a metal fence post driven into the earth. The bottom section of the telescope mast slips over this fence post and a very firm mounting is obtained for the light-weight PVC piping mast.

The two versions of Fig.8 produce excellent results considering the simplicity and limited mounting space required. A two-section mast is strictly self-supporting. A ten foot section of 2 inch ID PVC was telescoped two feet into a ten-foot section of 1.5 inch ID. The two sections were bolted together. Bolt separation was 8 inches. Two holes were drilled about two foot above the bottom of the lower section. These two holes separated by about 1½ inch will hold the connection bolts to which the transmission line, helical wire and earth are attached. As per the previous helical vertical the inner conductor of the coax and the helical wire are joined at the top bolt. The earth wire and the coaxial braid are joined at the bottom bolt.

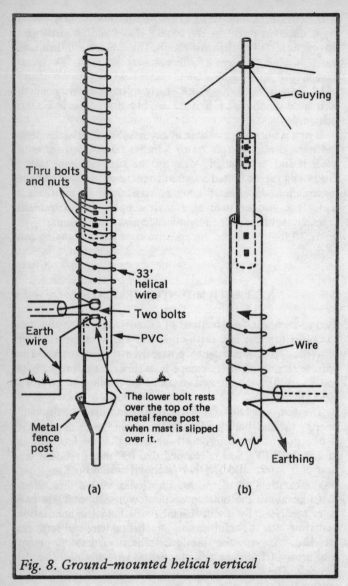

Fig. 8. Ground-mounted helical vertical

28

The separation between loops for bottom 10-foot section is 6 inches. Along the top section decrease the spacing to accommodate the full length of the helical wire. In our example a 33-foot length of helical wire was used. This length corresponds to a quarter-wavelength on 41 metres. An acceptable earth is attained using the same length of wire wound around the bottom 2-foot section of the mast and then laid in straightline fashion about 2 inches under the earth. A more balanced earth plane can be attained by using at least three earth radials.

Excellent results were obtained on bands 11 through 31 metres. Often the aerial, as characteristic of verticals, permits understandable signal reception when a band is just opening to a particular section of the earth. Reasonable results were also obtained on some of the lower-frequency bands.

To improve results, work progressed to a three section vertical as shown in Fig. 8b. In this arrangement a 60-foot length of helical wire was used corresponding to a quarter-wavelength on 75 metres. The telescoping aerial consisted of the two lower sections used previously in example (a) and a top section with an outer diameter of 1¼ inch. Spacing between loops was again 6 inches along the bottom section and then gradually tapered over the top sections to accommodate the full 60-foot length of helical-wound wire. The mast can be guyed several feet down from the very top using plastic, nylon or polyester line. If you use plastic clothesline be certain it does not have a metallic core. The three-mast arrangement did result in a decided improvement in bands 60 through 120 metres as compared to example (a).

9.   RANDOM WIRE AND TUNER

A random length wire in conjunction with a tuner can provide acceptable to good performance at a difficult mounting site. A tuner is especially useful in receiving the low-frequency short-wave bands when using a short aerial. The improvements that a tuner offers are better performance with a short aerial, better results in the reception of weak signals, minimization of

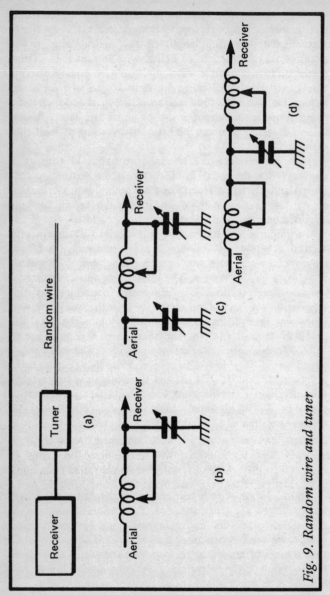

Fig. 9. Random wire and tuner

the effects of fast-fade and selective fading for the SWL that prefers a rock-solid performance from even a strong signal (music fan) and improvement when using a receiver of limited sensitivity and/or one subject to image reception.

In using a short aerial and random wire arrangement, as shown in Fig.9, the random wire is connected to the single-wire input of the tuner. Tuner output connects to receiver. Three common tuner circuits are shown. Example (b) consists of a tapped coil and variable capacitor. The Pi-net of (c) is perhaps the most popular, presenting a lower impedance path for the resonant signal and rejecting off-frequency signals more effectively. Our personal preference is the T-net arrangement of (d) It consists of tapped inductors and a single variable capacitor. The sharp selectivity and range of frequencies over which the performance is sharp are impressive.

In general, when adjusting a tuner, the capacitors are first set to mid-scale. Then the inductor tap is moved to a setting of maximum signal. Now the variable capacitors are tuned for peak performance. On occasion you can obtain a slightly better signal by bracketing the inductor. This means try the inductor setting on each side of the previous one and retune the capacitors. However, optimum results are usually obtained with the first position.

In a comparison test a 20-foot single-wire aerial was connected to the random wire input of the tuner and a second 20-foot length of wire to the inner conductor of a two-position coaxial switch. The output of the tuner was connected to the receiver input. The output of the coaxial switch was connected to the receiver input. Using the type (c) Pi-net type of tuner, impressive results were obtained. As was to be expected, this improvement was pronounced on bands 41 through 120 metres. Results on other bands varied from none, limited, to significant improvement. Only one band showed a decline that might indicate that the tuner itself did not peak sharply on that range.

Tuner (d) is not quite as convenient because there are two tapped inductors. More testing is involved because you must bracket two inductors in searching for the highest peak.

Here is a special general tip in using a tuner with various

aerial types. The short-wave broadcast bands occupy quite a spread of frequencies and, on occasion on some bands, the combination of aerial resistance and length of coaxial transmission line accent attenuation. Look into the matter if signal level on a particular band, when making comparison checks with another aerial, is much lower than seems sensible. A tuner helps in such a spot. However the problem can also be handled by adding or subtracting a quarter-wave section in coaxial line in the overall span of line between aerial and receiver. Make this line segment a quarter-wavelength on the troublesome band. Use the simple equation:

$$\text{Length (feet)} = (246/f_{MHz}) \times 0.66$$

10. END FED WAVELENGTH AERIAL

The end-fed wire aerial, Fig.10, has always been a popular one for DX reception. If it is not of proper length, a somewhat spotty performance is sometimes obtained from band to band. The occasional bad spots in sensitivity can be the result of the very high impedance found at the end of an aerial when its overall length is any multiple of a half-wavelength. However, by proper selection of overall length this tendency can be minimized. In our tests an end-fed wire about 102 foot long performed well. This length resonated as a full wavelength on a frequency somewhat lower than the 31 metre band. Although detailed tests were not made, good all-band performance was obtained. Some weak directions were indicated on the higher frequency bands. Although not serious they do indicate the presence of some multiple lobing as is to be anticipated when a horizontal aerial is a number of wavelengths long. Fortunately the low height of a typical long-wire aerial used for DXing reduces the severity of any such nodes in the sensitivity pattern.

The critical DXer can eke out additional signal level and stability with the use of a tuner. However, results vary from none, a bit, to significant improvement depending upon frequency and direction of signal arrival. Such results are to be

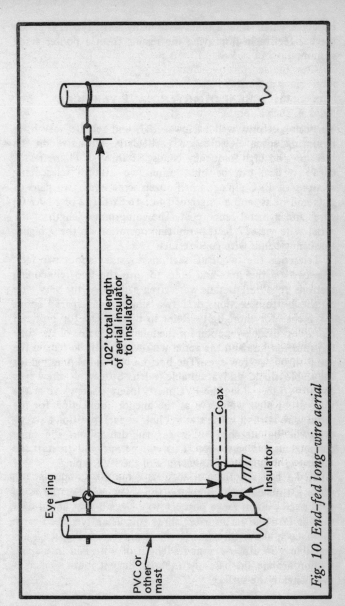

Fig. 10. End-fed long-wire aerial

expected when using a tuner with many aerial types. They are most effective in improving the results from a poorer aerial system.

11. CHEAP QUARTER-WAVE VERTICAL

Verticals perform well as low aerials and require very little mounting space. Results are particularly attractive on the medium and high-frequency bands, 31 through 11 metres. A cheap vertical can be built using two 10-foot telescoping sections of PVC piping, a half-dozen screw-eyes, two pairs of nuts and bolts, and a length of 14 or 16 SWG (12 or 14 AWG) wire, and a metal fence post. The compromise length of the aerial wire was 17 feet, permitting operation on the 7 higher frequency bands with good results.

Telescope the two PVC sections together about two feet. Use two of the nuts and bolts to firm the two telescoping sections together. Details were given earlier. At the very base of the bottom section, drill two single holes spaced about 1.5 inches for short bolts. Refer to Fig.11. The top bolt and nut will provide a junction for the inner conductor of the coax transmission line and the aerial wire which will be fed up the aerial through screw-eyes. The bottom bolt is the junction for the cable shield and a suitable earth. Space the screw-eyes about two feet along the PVC mast. Insert a screw-eye at the very top which will serve as the anchor connection for the aerial wire. Drill a single starting hole at each position a screw-eye will be attached using a small drill about the same diameter as the screw-eye. This will permit you to start the screw-eye through the hard surface of the PVC piping.

String the aerial wire through the screw eyes, pull tight and make a firm connection to the top screw-eye. Set the aerial pole over a metal fence post. Drive a ground post about 6 or so feet into the earth or use three equidistantly spaced earth wires, each about the same length as the aerial. If space is not available you can use a single length of wire laid in a spiral fashion around the base of the aerial. Bury it about an inch or two beneath the surface.

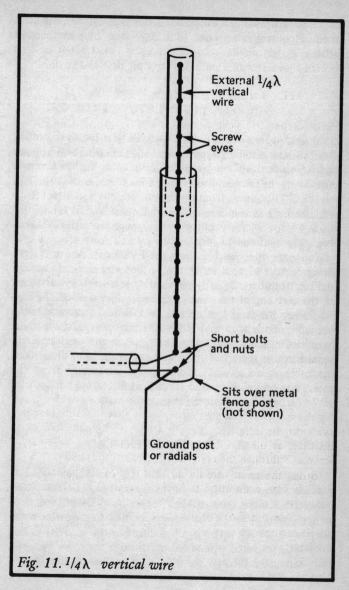

Fig. 11. $^1/_4\lambda$ vertical wire

Often a simple vertical aerial of this type can be suspended from an outrigger attached to a high point of a dwelling. A similar aerial can be constructed using two 10-foot battens bolted together with a suitable mounting base and guying.

12. DOUBLE OR TRIPLE PVC VERTICAL

The performance of the quarter-wave vertical can be smoothed out over the seven high-frequency bands by using two or more individual verticals cut from insulated wire. The PVC piping makes this aerial plan a simple and inexpensive construction, see Fig.12. Three individual verticals are cut and attached to the hot bolt at the base of the PVC mast. Aerial lengths are 13.5, 17 and 24 feet, they are fed through the series of screw-eyes. The 13.5 and 17 foot lengths are tied down at screw-eyes placed near these heights along the PVC mast. Above the tie-down for the 17 foot aerial, the 24 foot wire is wound around the top of the mast, finally terminating at a screw-eye attached at the very top of the mast. This aerial does well on the high frequency bands and often can be mounted just outside the window of your ground floor listening post. Only a short length of coaxial cable brings the signal to the receiver. Earth system can be three lengths of wire cut to the same dimensions as the three aerial wires and spaced equidistantly about the base of the mast. If limited space is available use a single wire of 24 feet spiraled about the base of the mast.

13. UMBRELLA VERTICAL

The basic idea of aerials 11 and 12 can be extended to include some of the lower-frequency bands. The basic umbrella constructions of Fig.13 show how. Overall length of aerial wire will be 39 feet, corresponding to a quarter wavelength on the 49 metre band. A single 14 or 16 SWG (12 or 14 AWG) insulated wire is fed up through the screw-eyes to a bolt connected through the PVC mast at the very top. Overall length of this section of the aerial will be approximately 18

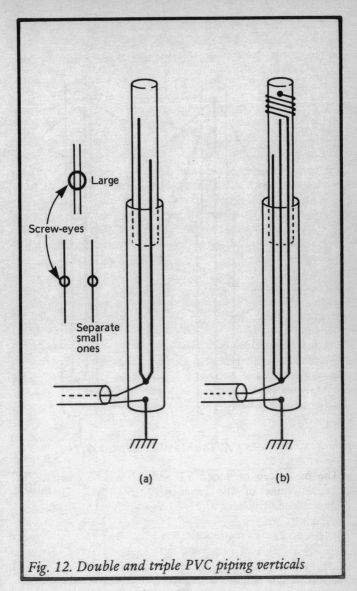

Fig. 12. Double and triple PVC piping verticals

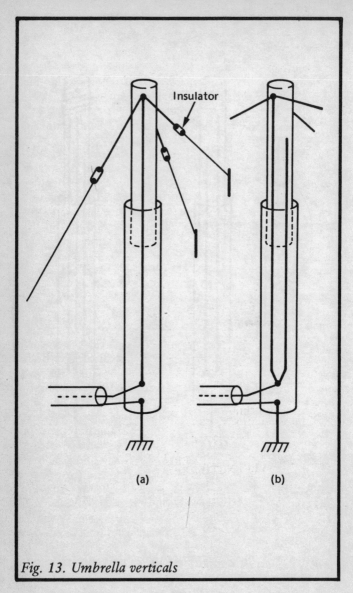

Insulator

(a)   (b)

Fig. 13. Umbrella verticals

38

feet. Three additional lengths of wire are now connected to the top bolt. These wires can be of smaller diameter. The length of each wire will be approximately 21 feet. They extend down from the mast and attach to individual insulators which are then linked by ropes to fence posts driven into the earth. The individual segments are spaced equidistantly (120°) about the mast. Use lengths of rope that stretch individual aerial lines as far out as possible away from the mast depending upon space available.

The above construction provides additional good performance on the 41 and 49 metre bands. Also acceptable performance is obtained on bands 60 through 120 metres, although you cannot expect signal levels to be as good as those obtained from long aerials cut to these low and very low frequency bands. Performance can be smoothed out on the high frequency bands by also using an additional 17-foot quarterwave vertical that extends up the mast as shown in example (b).

14. MULTIBAND UMBRELLA

The aerial of Fig.14 further extends the umbrella concept for low-band reception in a limited space. Four individual verticals are involved, cut to 13.5, 24, 39 and 59 feet. The latter corresponds to a quarter wavelength on the 75 metre band. Acceptable results are obtained on the 90 and 120 metre bands although, if space is available, you may give some thought to using a length of 71 feet for the fourth vertical. In our check aerial 18 SWG (16 AWG) stranded insulated wire was used. This umbrella resulted in a significant boost in low-frequency results without taking up a lot of ground area.

Individual verticals were fed through the eye rings as in the construction of the vertical of Fig.12. One wire extended up the mast to about 13.5 feet. The remaining three extended to eye-rings at the very top and then spanned out in umbrella-like fashion.

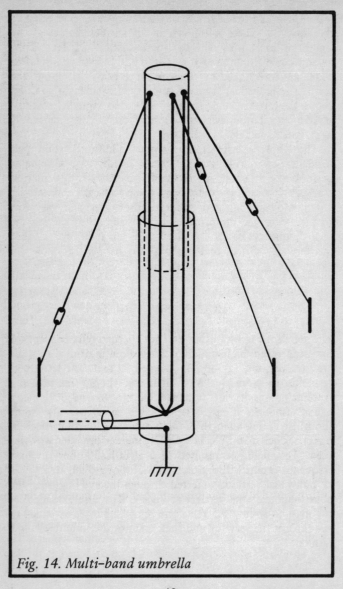

Fig. 14. Multi-band umbrella

15. 11 AND 13 METRE QUARTER-WAVE SPECIAL

Combined interest in aerials and propagation make the 11 and
13 metre bands attractive. The omnidirectional and low-angle
attributes of the vertical are ideal for these bands. Elevating
the vertical helps. Two PVC pipes with inner diameters of 1.25
and 1 inch along with a 10-foot section of thin-walled
aluminum tubing with an outer diameter of 7/8 inch make
this possible as shown in Fig.15. The overall length of the
aluminum tubing is 10 feet which is a good compromise for
quarter-wave operation on 11 and 13 metres.

The aluminum tubing was telescoped about 2 feet into
smaller diameter PVC pipe and bolted fast. The bottom
holding bolt was placed about ½ inch above the bottom of the
aluminum element. This serves as the hot connection. About
1.5 inches below this bolt a second hole was drilled through
the PVC piping. Four radial wires were connected to this bolt.
Inner conductor and coaxial shield attach to the hot and radial
bolts respectively. Electrical tape is used to hold the coaxial
line along the mast. The four radial wires and appropriate
insulators along with nylon rope extend down to ground
stakes. An ideal match is made to 50-ohm coaxial line. This is
a good aerial for 11 and 13 metres, reaching out for those
early openings to various parts of the world.

16. TRIANGLE

The triangle, Fig.16, is a low-cost wire aerial that has some
directivity and performs very well on the band to which it is
cut. It requires little space, only a single mast and is easy to
erect. Good performance is also obtained on the two adjacent
bands and an acceptable performance on other bands. Drop-
off in sensitivity is more pronounced on the bands located on
the low-frequency side of the resonant band.

It is a full-wavelength aerial, like the quad and delta loop,
without being so clumsy and subject to weather damage. The
very centre of the full-wavelength wire is attached at the top
of the support mast. When using PVC mast, this can be an eye

41

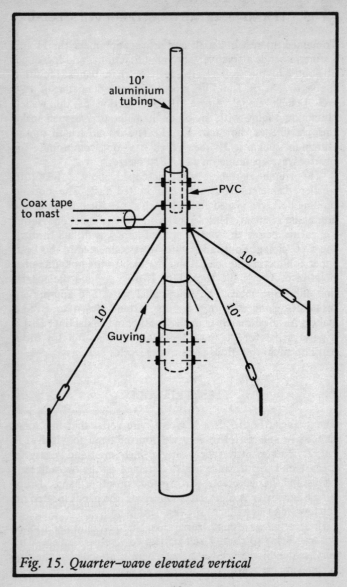

Fig. 15. Quarter–wave elevated vertical

42

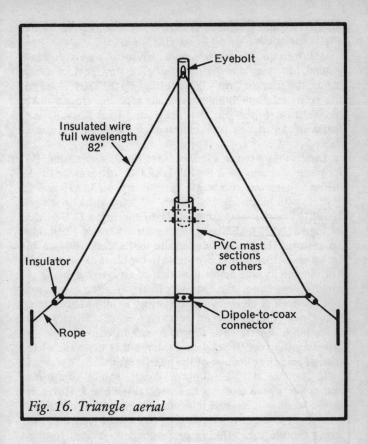

Fig. 16. Triangle aerial

bolt. The two legs fan out and fold back on themselves. The
ends are returned to the mast to a dipole connector or to a
pair of bolt/nut combinations mounted in the PVC mast.
Coaxial or TV line can be used.

The triangle is stretched out on each side using nylon rope
and two metal fence posts. You will find it is a very rigid
assembly with the support lines acting as partial guying for a
high mast. It is not necessary that the triangle be equal-sided
(equilateral). In some mounting situations it may be advantageous to have the triangle base a different length than the

43

sides. The important thing is to have the wire loop resonate as a full-wavelength loop on a preferred band.

A low-frequency triangle need only be 7 to 8 feet above ground, just clear of pedestrian traffic. On the higher frequency bands, the triangle base will be further up the mast. However, the same technique using appropriate rope and ground stakes can be used to pull out the triangle and tie it down. Overall length of the triangle is given in the full wavelength column of Table 5.

Dimensions given in Fig.16 are for the 25 metre band. Performance was also good for 31, 41 and 49 metres as well as 19 metres. There was acceptable performance on 11, 13 and 16 metres with declining results on 60 through 120 metres. Sensitivity-wise it was comparable to the triple PVC vertical of Fig.12, with somewhat poor results on bands 11 through 16 metres. There was also definite useful directivity on the crowded 25 metre band broadside to the plane of the triangle. This directivity was better than that of an inverted dipole cut for the same band. Also gain was better than the comparison PVC vertical. A bit more sensitivity may or may not be useful. Sometimes the important advantage is one that permits reduction of interference coming from a differing direction by orienting the triangle in such a manner that the plane of the triangle is in the direction of the interference.

In checking out the full-wave triangle loop by comparison with other types a more subtle advantage was heard. This reception advantage is perhaps obvious with other full-wavelength loops such as a quad or delta loop and maybe related to their larger capture area. During propagation conditions troubled with sharp and fast fading there was less pumping and, on occasion, the range over which the fade occurred, amplitude-wise, was not as pronounced. Such a favorable attribute results in less selective fade distortion and an improvement in musical and vocal clarity. However limited the improvement, such could be of significant help in making a difficult identification.

17. HIGH-FREQUENCY TRIANGLE

A shorter 55-foot triangle Fig.17a, was cut for the 16 metre band. Good 11 through 19 metre performance resulted. Directivity was quite obvious on 16 metres.

As shown in Fig.17b, the two triangles can be mounted on the same mast. For optimum results you can use two individual coaxial transmission lines. An alternative is to link the two feed points with a 300-ohm parallel line. Attach the coaxial line to lower feed point. Some experimentation with the overall length of the connecting line may be necessary to obtain the most uniform results over the shortwave bands. However you may prefer to adjust this length to peak performance on the two preferred bands.

18. TILTED 3/2-WAVELENGTH AERIAL

The 3/2-wavelength aerial as described previously has a low impedance feedpoint at the centre and 3/4-wavelength legs. Such an aerial can be made more directive by tilting the legs forward as shown in Fig.18. When the legs are tilted forward horizontally, the aerial displays maximum sensitivity along the line that bisects the included angle. Angle should be approximately 100°. As shown in the pattern there are minor side and back lobes which does give the aerial multidirectional characteristics as well.

Leg length for the 16 metre band would be approximately 40 feet long. Some trimming of leg lengths can be helpful in finding band resonance. You must use a comparison aerial. Note that this same leg length also corresponds to the length of a dipole element on the 49 metre band. Consequently the aerial performs well over much of the shortwave broadcast spectrum. Cut with 73 foot elements you would have a 3/2-wavelength aerial on 31 metres and a dipole on 90 metres, extending good sensitivity up into the very low frequency bands.

This aerial requires three separate masts. Again PVC piping is an easy way to go. At the dipole frequency the aerial is

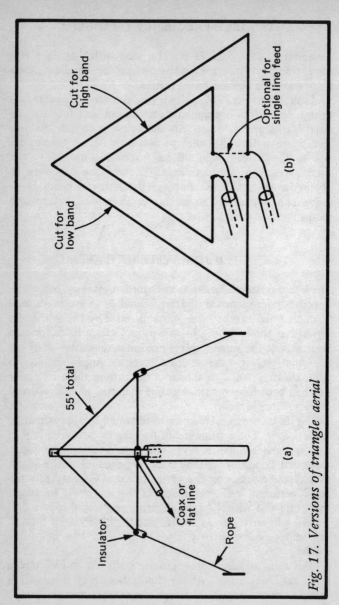

Fig. 17. Versions of triangle aerial

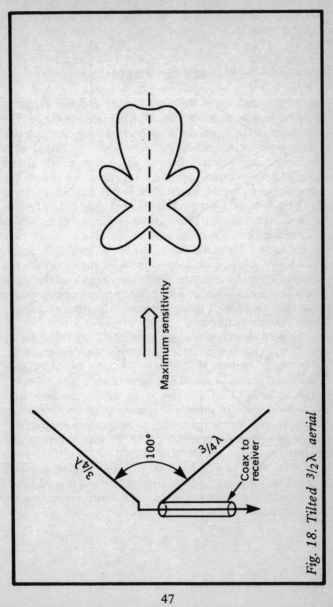

Maximum sensitivity

3/4λ

3/4λ

100°

Coax to receiver

Fig. 18. Tilted 3/2λ aerial

essentially omnidirectional, becoming more directional at higher frequencies.

19.   VEE-BEAM AERIALS

Higher gain and more directivity can be obtained from the tilted leg plan by increasing overall leg length, see Fig.19. The impedance at the feedpoint drops to a minimum for each odd quarter-wave of overall length. The chart associated with Fig.19 lists approximate favored angle between aerial legs along with approximate gain for the leg length indicated. The angle must be decreased as the leg length is increased. In so doing the sensitivity pattern sharpens and a higher gain results. In most situations for broadcast reception the directivity is of more significance than the gain.

The Table 5 dimension chart helps in determining leg length while a good compass will help you with the angular orientation of masts when you erect the aerial. The compass will help you locate the centre line that is to point the favorite direction at your mounting site. A little right-angle trigonometry helps to locate the mast positions.

The previous 3/2-wavelength aerial of 73 feet length for 31 metres was indicated in Table 5. A quarter-wave dimension for 16 metres is 14 feet. Multiply this figure by five to obtain a 5/4-wavelength of 70 feet. The suggested angle for a 5/4-wavelength aerial is 85°. Consequently by moving the two outer masts nearer to each other it is possible to set-up a Vee-beam aerial for a 16 metre operation. A compromise angle of 90° produces a good performance on 16, 31 and 90 metres, and the aerial performs well on other bands too.

If you want to eke out the very best performance you might consider using low-loss parallel line and a good tuner. Such manner of operation is not a necessity unless you are most critical of results.

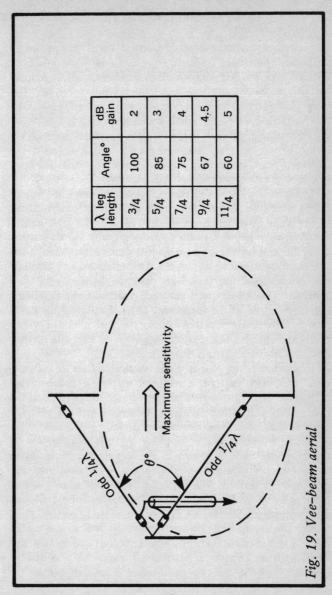

λ leg length	Angle°	dB gain
3/4	100	2
5/4	85	3
7/4	75	4
9/4	67	4.5
11/4	60	5

Fig. 19. Vee–beam aerial

49

20. TWO IN-PHASE VERTICALS

As described earlier the basic vertical aerial has an omni-directional horizontal radiation pattern and good low-angle vertical pick-up. Gain as well as a horizontal directional pattern can be obtained by using two or more verticals. The basic plan for two in-phase verticals is given in Fig.20a. The two verticals are spaced a half wavelength and fed in-phase. Two identical lengths of cable feed the separate quarter-wave verticals from the main transmission line that connects to the receiver. Thus an incoming signal travels exactly the same length to the junction and becomes additive.

The aerial system is directional broadside to the plane of the two verticals. Signals arriving in either direction broadside to the plane travel the same length of line to the junction and consequently they are additive. However, any signals arriving along the line of the two verticals become subtractive at the feedpoint because one of the signals must travel an additional half wavelength which is the distance between the two verticals. This latter signal subtracts from the signal striking the first vertical at the feedpoint. The net result of the aerial plan is a figure-eight pattern similar to that obtained with a horizontal dipole. This pattern is shown in Fig. 20a looking down on the two verticals, 1 and 2.

In summary, the two in-phase vertical results in a figure-eight sensitivity pattern. Sensitivity pattern is bi-directional with gain that is broadside (perpendicular) to the plane of the two verticals. It is least sensitive to signals arriving near the angle of the line between the two verticals.

The arrangement of two in-phase verticals for operation on the 16 metre band is shown in Fig.20b. In the construction two pieces of telescoping PVC piping were used for each quarter-wave vertical. The verticals themselves were made of insulated wire held to each of the PVC masts with screw eyes. Compromise length of 13.1 feet was used and provided good results on the 13 and 19 metre bands as well as on the 16 metre band. Separation was 28 feet, corresponding to a half wavelength on 16 metres. A coaxial T connector provided the junction between the two equal-length lines that run to the

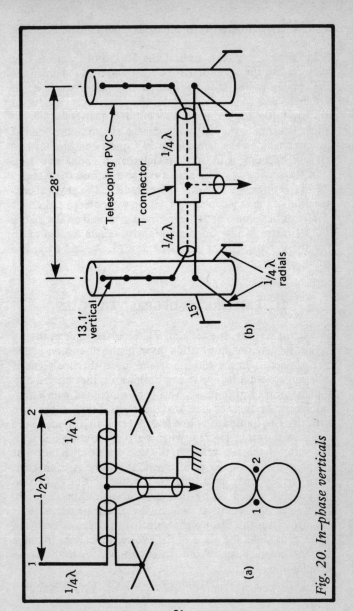

Fig. 20. In-phase verticals

separate verticals and the main coaxial transmission line back to the receiver.

In constructing each vertical the 13.1 foot length is first connected to the very top of the mast and then fed down the PVC piping as far as it will go. At this point two bolt/nut terminals are constructed. Note that the inner conductor attaches to the top terminal. A set of three, quarter-wavelength radials attaches to the bottom terminal and also to the braid of the coaxial line. The telescoping PVC mast consisted of two ten-foot sections with sections telescoped about two feet. Thus the vertical is well elevated and also permits the fanning-out of the three equidistantly spaced radials. The physical construction of the telescoping PVC piping was covered earlier.

The vertical combination performed very well on the 13, 16 and 19 metre bands. Good results with only a limited or no directivity were also obtained on the 11, 25 and 31 metre bands.

21. END-FIRE 180-DEGREE VERTICALS

Except for phasing, the aerial of Fig.21 is the same as that of Fig.20. Review the information given in the discussion of the previous aerial. In the end-fire arrangement, the two verticals are again spaced a half-wavelength. However, they are fed out-of-phase instead of in-phase. This is accomplished with a half-wavelength section of line that connects between the two verticals. The transmission line is connected to just one of the aerials as shown in Fig.21a. When a signal arrives in-line with the plane of the two verticals, the two signals are additive at the point to which the main transmission line is connected. When signals arrive broadside to the two verticals, the two components picked up by the separate verticals become sub-tractive at the point at which the main transmission is attached. Thus the figure-eight sensitivity pattern as shown in (a) extends along the plane of the two verticals. Note that it is just the complement of the pattern shown for the in-phase combination of Fig.20.

A practical way of obtaining out-of-phase feed is shown in

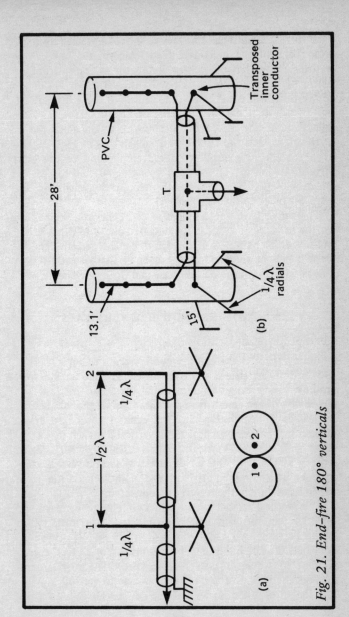

Fig. 21. End-fire 180° verticals

Fig.21b. The additional 180^u phase shift is obtained by transposing one of the individual feed lines to just one of the verticals. Note that the centre conductor as traced from the centre of the T connector is fed to the aerial portion of the left vertical, while it is fed to the radials of the right vertical. The shield, as it did for the aerial of Fig.20, connects to the radials of the left aerial while it connects to the aerial proper of the right vertical. The aerial arrangements of Figs. 20 and 21 are identical except for the feed method to the right vertical. If you erect this aerial you will be able to flip the directional pattern conveniently simply by changing the manner of feed to the right vertical.

The aerials have a figure-eight pattern. However the pattern for the in-phase verticals is an elongated one, while that of the end-fire combination is a broad figure-eight pattern. The in-phase combination has a higher gain and a sharper pattern than that obtained with the out-of-phase end-fire arrangement.

22.   END-FIRE 90-DEGREE VERTICALS

A good performing vertical combination that requires little mounting space is the end-fire configuration of Fig.22. When two verticals are spaced a quarter-wavelength and fed $90°$ they produce a very broad uni-directional (cardioid) pattern. The directivity of the aerials is in the direction of the $90°$ lagging vertical as shown in Fig.22a. The section of coaxial transmission line between vertical 1 and vertical 2 is such that a $90°$ phase shift results. Vertical 2 lags vertical 1 by $90°$. Signal arriving at the right side of the aerial generates vertical components which are additive at the point where the main transmission line to the receiver is connected.

The physical arrangement of the two telescoping masts and the 13.1 feet verticals, Fig.22b, is identical to that described in the previous two aerials discussions, 20 and 21. However, note that the spacing is only 14 feet instead of 28 feet, corresponding to a quarter-wavelength in space. The coaxial transmission line back to the receiver connects to vertical 1. A 15-foot length of 300-ohm TV flat line connects between vertical

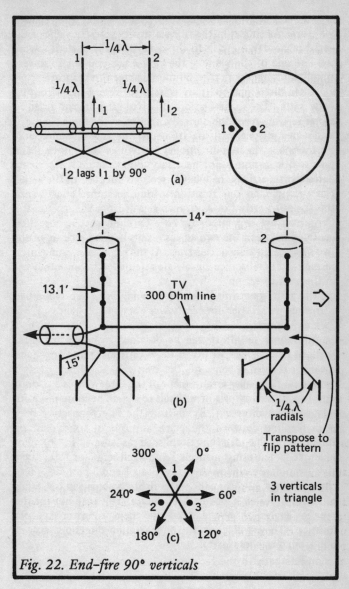

Fig. 22. End-fire 90° verticals

1 and vertical 2. This connection takes care of the required 90° feed. As shown in (b) the sensitivity is to the right of the aerial plane. If you wish to flip-over the entire pattern toward the left side of the plane of the two aerials you can do so very simply by transposing the 300-ohm line feed to vertical 2.

A uni-directional pattern is said to have a high front-to-back ratio. The combination also has gain. It can accent a signal arriving from the desired direction at the same time as it attenuates a signal arriving from just the opposite direction. Furthermore the uni-directional pattern is quite broad and precise orientation is not necessary. Furthermore it accommodates signals arriving in many directions forward of the aerial. For example, in our location in Southeastern Pennsylvania, the angles of arrival of Australian signals from Shepparton and Carnarvon are separated by 71°. Cardioid pattern direction centered between the two angles results in good pick-up of the two Australian transmitter sites. At the same time, some interfering medium-distance signals are attenuated because they are in the back direction.

The aerial performed well on 16 and 19 metres. Good performance with lesser directivity was obtained on bands 11, 13, 25 and 31.

Additional versatility can be obtained by mounting three verticals in a triangle, or use just two verticals and a convenient means of moving one of the verticals to either of two positions. Triangular arrangement of the three verticals permits one to choose any pair of verticals to obtain maximum sensitivity in given direction. By shifting the interconnecting 300-ohm feedline between the pairs, any one of six maximum-direction angles can be established as shown in (c). For example, when using verticals 1 and 2, either 0° or 180° directivity can be obtained. Use of verticals 1 and 3 permits you to choose either 120° or 300°. The final combination of aerials of 2 and 3 permit a 60° or 240° choice. You need not use the precise angles shown, instead fit them to your specific location. They will provide six maximum directions spaced 60° around the compass.

23. DIPOLE AND PARASITIC REFLECTOR

A parasitic aerial element has no direct connection with the dipole element to which the transmission line is attached. A parasitic reflector is cut longer than the connected element. Maximum directivity is broadside in a line extending from the reflector to the connected element as shown in Fig.23a. The spacing between the connected and parasitic elements falls between 0.1 and 0.25 wavelength. Measurements for parasitic directors and reflectors are given in Table 5 along with dimensions for various spacings between a quarter wavelength and 0.1 wavelength.

In terms of short-wave listening a directive and parasitic element combination can be erected to favor some preferred direction or individual station. At the same time, such an aerial has reasonable sensitivity to signals arriving at other angles. Two least sensitive directions are in line with the plane of the aerial. Good results can be obtained by aligning this plane in the precise direction of a station that gives you troublesome interference when you are trying to receive a preferred station. In short-wave listening it is often advantageous to decrease the level of the undesired signal at the same time you try to boost the desired signal as much as feasible. It is the combination that does the job with emphasis on decreasing the undesired signal level to as low a value as possible.

Dimensions in Fig.23 are given for a parasitic reflector and dipole combination for the 25 metre band. Four individual masts are involved. They can be the light-weight PVC types as covered previously. A compromise alternative is to use an inverted dipole and inverted reflector as shown in Fig.23b. Only two masts are required. The ends of the inverted elements are brought down to short fence posts. Ends are accessible and can be trimmed for optimum results. Dimensions are given for the 25 metre band.

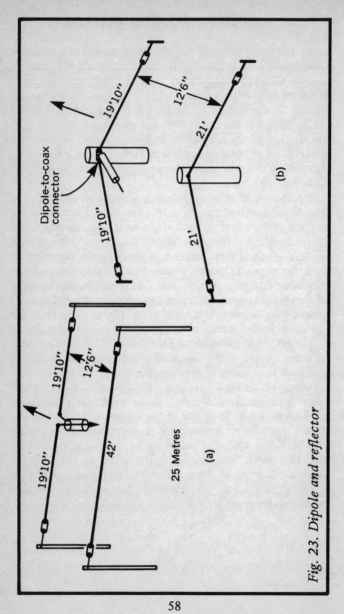

Dipole-to-coax connector

19'10"

19'10"

12'6"

42'

25 Metres

(a)

19'10"

19'10"

12'6"

21'

21'

(b)

Fig. 23. Dipole and reflector

24. DIPOLE AND PARASITIC DIRECTOR

A parasitic director is cut shorter than the connected element. In this case, the maximum directivity is in a line broadside from the connected element through the director, Fig.24a. To save space the parasitic director can be brought near to the connected element. Minimum spacing is approximately 0.1 wavelengths. This short spacing is used for the 49 metre aerial given in (a).

An interesting 31 metre combination is shown in Fig.24b. Note that the driven element can be changed over in its overall length by connecting and disconnecting a jumper between the two inner insulators. With the two jumpers open the parasitic element acts as a director with maximum pick-up in the direction from the connected element toward the director. When the jumpers are closed, the parasitic element acts as a reflector and directivity flips over with maximum direction between the reflector toward the connected element. The parasitic element can be mounted with a halyard arrangement attached to the parasitic element masts. Thus it can be raised and lowered to make the jumper change.

25. ED NOLL'S AUSTRALIA/SPAIN SPECIAL

In addition to the fine programming of the Australian and Spanish short-wave broadcast systems, there are two other favorable attributes for setting up a good performing aerial here in Southeastern, Pennsylvania, U.S.A. Australian broadcast system has multiband capabilities and a transmitter site more than 10,000 miles from my receiving site. Ideal for aerial checking! Although Spain is only 3700 miles away, I like Spanish music. Most helpful are the azimuth bearings, 65° to Spain and 260° to Australia. The angular separation is but 15° shy of 180°. Consequently an aerial system with a sensitivity pattern that can be flipped over conveniently is attractive for the reception of both Australia and Spain. In considering an aerial for two or more of your favorite stations, you may be able to use the ideas that are a part of my special aerial.

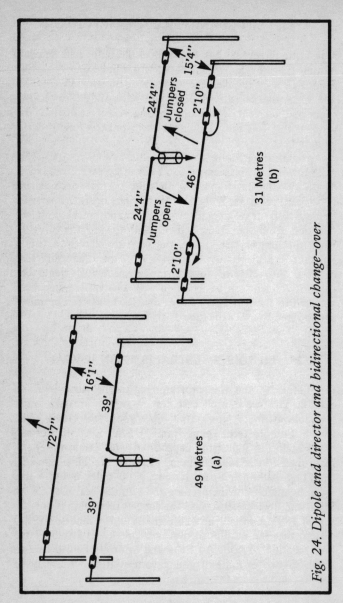

Fig. 24. Dipole and director and bidirectional change–over

An earlier aerial discussed the characteristics of two phased quarterwave verticals fed 90°, Fig.22. It was a simple matter to flip over the attractive 90° cardioid pattern. The aerial of Fig.25 uses three such quarter-wavelength verticals. They provide more gain than a single pair. The resultant cardioid pattern is not as broad but the excellent front-to-back ratio remains.

In a three-vertical combination the array is connected to the transmission line at vertical 2. Vertical 1 is connected 90° lagging using a quarterwave section of 300-ohm TV line that is not transposed. Vertical 3 must be fed in such a manner that it is 270° lagging vertical 2. The net result will be to have vertical 2 lag vertical 3 by 90°. This is accomplished by using a quarterwave section of line that is transposed as shown in Fig.25a. Using vertical 3 as a starting point, you will note that vertical 2 lags vertical 3 by 90° and vertical 1 lags vertical 2 by 90°. This feed arrangement displays maximum sensitivity toward Spain when the three verticals are lined up in that direction.

A single 15-foot ground radial was used for verticals 1 and 3. These were dropped to the ground and then buried two inches below the surface in a direction away from the other verticals but in a direction in line with the verticals as shown in Fig.25a. Two 15-foot radials were connected to vertical 2 and positioned opposite to each other but in line with the verticals. As a result a like radial system is installed stretching out toward Spain and Ausralia.

The complete pattern can be flipped over in the direction of Australia by reversing the TV line connections at verticals 1 and 3 as shown in Fig.25b. In this arrangement vertical 3 is connected 90° lagging while vertical 1 is connected 270° lagging. Starting at vertical 1 you will find that vertical 2 lags vertical 1 by 90° and vertical 3 lags vertical 2 by 90°. Consequently the pattern is oriented toward Australia.

The aerial as dimensioned provides gain and good directivity on 16, 19 and 25 metre bands. There is limited directivity (more bi-directional) on 11, 13 and 31 metre bands. Acceptable omnidirection results are obtained on 41 and 49 metre bands.

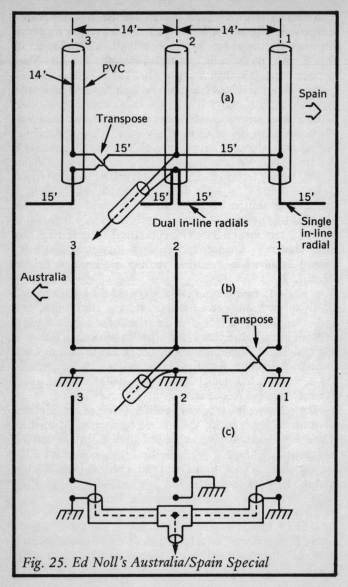

Fig. 25. Ed Noll's Australia/Spain Special

Since the two outer verticals are spaced by a half wavelength they can be centre-fed to obtain a broadside pattern when connected in-phase as shown in Fig.25c. This manner of feeding only the two outer verticals establishes a bi-directional directivity that is broadside to the plane of the verticals.

Put some thought to the matter and you will no doubt come up with a simple little-space aerial structure that will permit you to favor some favorites at your own location. Aerial experimentation is fun!

Notes

Please note overleaf is a list of other titles that are available in our range of Radio, Electronics and Computer Books.

These should be available from all good Booksellers, Radio Component Dealers and Mail Order Companies.

However, should you experience difficulty in obtaining any title in your area, then please write directly to the publisher enclosing payment to cover the cost of the book plus adequate postage.

If you would like a complete catalogue of our entire range of Radio, Electronics and Computer Books then please send a Stamped Addressed Envelope to:

BERNARD BABANI (publishing) LTD
THE GRAMPIANS
SHEPHERDS BUSH ROAD
LONDON W6 7NF
ENGLAND